BATTLE™

ANNUAL

ANNUAL

ISBN: 9781783294671

Published by Titan Books,
A division of Titan Publishing Group Ltd.
144 Southwark Street
London SE1 0UP

A CIP catalogue record for this title is available from the British Library.

First published: October 2014
10 9 8 7 6 5 4 3 2 1
Printed in Italy.

What did you think of this book? We love to hear from our readers.
Please email us at: **readerfeedback@titanemail.com**, or write to us at
the above address.

To receive advance information, news, competitions, and exclusive Titan
offers online, please register as a member by clicking the "sign up"
button on our website: **www.titanbooks.com**

Much of the comic strip source material used by Titan Books in this edition
is exceedingly rare. As such, we hope that readers appreciate that the
quality of reproduction achievable can vary.

BATTLE™ ANNUAL

TITAN BOOKS

ROLL CALL

D-DAY DAWSON

"THAT'S THE WAY I WANT TO GO OUT – FIGHTING!"

Nothing was going to stop Sgt Steve Dawson from fighting alongside his men — not even the German bullet lodged close to his heart that had given him just a year left to live, and nothing to lose. Now, there's no mission too daring, and no odds too small: he's going to fight the Hun 'til his last breath, or die trying! During its run of two series and nearly two years, from 8 March 1975 to 22 January 1977, 'D-Day Dawson' regularly fought the 'Rat Pack' for top-dog status in *Battle*'s readers' poll. Gerry Finley-Day and Ron Carpenter wrote the majority of the first series while Colin Page supplied most of the artwork. ✵

NOTES FROM THE FRONT LINE:

'We did have a lot of fun coming up with the characters, and although "D-Day Dawson" wasn't the very first created, he was certainly one of the earliest. We wanted a very archetypal comic character, which "D-Day Dawson" clearly is, and then we needed to give him an original spin and I think the idea of a guy with only a limited period of time to live seemed to fit the bill.

'We knew it would be very popular with the readers and that's why it was *Battle*'s lead story.

'We rather naively thought that 12 months would be enough for "Dawson", but the managing editor said: "No, this character is phenomenally popular, you've got to keep him going for ever!"' – Pat Mills

WRITTEN BY Gerry Finley-Day & Ron Carpenter
DRAWN BY Colin Page

D-DAY DAWSON

BEACH-HEAD!

THE 6th OF JUNE, 1944 – D-DAY! STEVE DAWSON IS JUST ONE OF A THOUSAND BRITISH SERGEANTS JUMPING ASHORE ON TO THE NORMANDY SANDS – BUT SOON HE IS TO BE A VERY DIFFERENT SOLDIER INDEED –

THE BIG DAY AT LAST, LADS! GIVE IT TO 'EM GOOD 'N' HOT!

YOU BET, SARGE!

TWO JERRY MACHINE GUN NESTS! WE'LL TAKE A FEW MEN EACH AND MOVE IN FROM THE SIDES, CORPORAL SPRING – TAKE 'EM BY SURPRISE.

RIGHT, SARGE!

SPRING'S GOT THE MAKINGS OF A GOOD FIGHTER. IF HE STAYS COOL WE'LL TAKE THOSE SPANDAUS EASY.

WE'RE THERE! LET 'EM HAVE IT, LADS!

BLITZEN! BRITISHERS!

AAAAGH!

THIS ONE'S CLEANED OUT, SARGE!

LOOK OUT, SPRING! ONE OF THOSE JERRIES IS STILL KICKING!

The warning yell made the German turn his attention to Dawson.

UGGH!

SPRING GOT THAT HUN, WHITEY.

BUT THAT AIN'T GOING TO HELP THE SARGE. HE LOOKS BAD. BETTER GET HIM TO ONE OF THE BOATS.

When Dawson came to, he was being taken off the beach.

I DON'T BELIEVE IT — I — I'M ALIVE. I THOUGHT THAT BULLET HAD MY NAME ON IT, DOC.

KEEP STILL, SERGEANT. YOU'RE HURT WORSE THAN YOU THINK . . .

THE BULLET'S LODGED NEXT TO YOUR HEART. IT'LL GET THERE SOONER OR LATER — AT THE MOST, MAYBE YOU'VE GOT A YEAR . . .

YOU MEAN I'VE HAD IT? BUT I FEEL FINE!

I'M SORRY, SERGEANT. THERE'S NOTHING WE CAN DO FOR YOU. YOU'RE BEING SENT HOME.

SO I'M A DYING MAN. IT — IT JUST DON'T MAKE SENSE. AN' THE LADS — SPRING, WHITEY . . . THEY'RE GOOD, BUT THEY'RE RAW. HOW CAN I LEAVE 'EM . . ?

Suddenly —

LOOK! THE GERMAN SHELLS ARE GETTING OUR RANGE! JUMP FOR IT!

JUMP I SAID!

THE WHOLE LANDING CRAFT'S GONE. THE POOR DEVILS. THEY WERE TOO SLOW.

SO NOW I'M THE ONLY ONE WHO KNOWS I'M DYING — AND MY MEN NEED HELP. THESE NAVY EXPLOSIVES'LL COME IN USEFUL.

D-DAY DAWSON

LOOK AT THE SARGE GO! HE'S AFRAID OF NOTHING!

SABOTAGE!

Nobody knows the truth about Sergeant Steve Dawson — that in the D-Day landings he took a German bullet near the heart that has given him less than a year to live. Now Dawson is leading his men on a mission to link up with glider troops at a vital bridge —

Soon — Dawson and his men reached their objective.

THERE'S THE DUVAL BRIDGE. WE'VE TO LINK UP WITH THE GLIDER TROOPS WHO'VE TAKEN IT AND GUARD IT FROM ANY ATTACK.

AAGH!

HOW D'YOU DO, SERGEANT DAWSON. YOU MISSED ALL THE REAL ACTION BUT I SUPPOSE JERRY MIGHT HAVE A CRACK AT BLOWING UP THE BRIDGE. KEEP YOUR MEN ON THEIR TOES, AND —

DAWSON — WHERE ARE YOU GOING?

Corporal Spring and Private White went with Dawson —

NO SIGN OF JERRIES ROUND HERE, SARGE.

CHECK ALONG THE RIVERBANK, SIR — JUST IN CASE.

HECK! THAT SLUG'S GETTIN' CLOSER TO MY HEART.

13

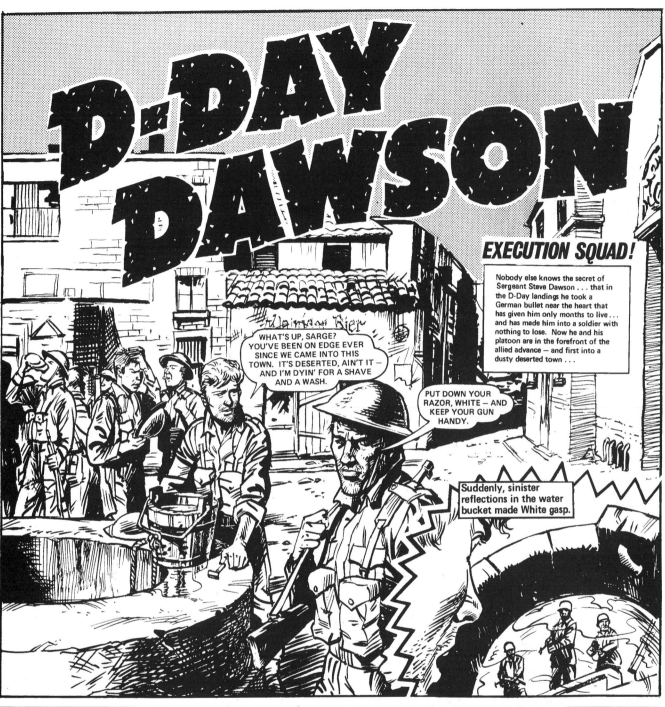

D-DAY DAWSON

EXECUTION SQUAD!

Nobody else knows the secret of Sergeant Steve Dawson . . . that in the D-Day landings he took a German bullet near the heart that has given him only months to live . . . and has made him into a soldier with nothing to lose. Now he and his platoon are in the forefront of the allied advance — and first into a dusty deserted town . . .

WHAT'S UP, SARGE? YOU'VE BEEN ON EDGE EVER SINCE WE CAME INTO THIS TOWN. IT'S DESERTED, AIN'T IT — AND I'M DYIN' FOR A SHAVE AND A WASH.

PUT DOWN YOUR RAZOR, WHITE — AND KEEP YOUR GUN HANDY.

Suddenly, sinister reflections in the water bucket made White gasp.

SARGE! ABOVE US!

GERMAN PARATROOPERS!

RIGHT INTO OUR TRAP, BRITISHERS. ONE WRONG MOVE AND YOU ARE ALL CORPSES!

NOW PITCH YOUR GUNS INTO THE WELL — QUICKLY!

THIS IS MY FAULT — NOT CHECKING THE ROOFS OUT. AND THESE PARAS ARE HARD TYPES — WHAT HAPPENS TO US NEXT?

Next instant Dawson had slashed out of his ropes and was diving sideways.

ACHTUNG! HE IS FREE!

DONE IT — MISSED THE WHOLE BURST. GOTTA FIND COVER FAST.

KILL THE SCHWEIN!

DOWN THIS WELL'S MY ONLY CHANCE! GOTTA DIVE DEEP.

But —

WE HAVE PUT TWO MAGAZINES DOWN THE WELL, HERR HAUPTMANN! HE MUST BE DEAD!

WE HAVE WASTED ENOUGH TIME! THE REST OF THE BRITISHERS — GET THEM OUT HERE.

YOUR MAD SERGEANT IS AT THE BOTTOM OF THE WELL!

WE STILL WON'T TALK, YOU MURDER-ING RATS!

VERY WELL — WIPE THEM ALL OUT! THESE ARE THEIR LAST SECONDS ON THIS EARTH!

NO . . . THEY'RE YOURS!

THE SARGE! HE'S ALIVE AN' GOT A GUN FROM THE WELL! LET'S TAKE 'EM!

COME ON! IT'S THEM OR US!

Fighting like desperate wildcats, Dawson's men soon overran the paratroopers —

THAT — THAT'S THE LOT, WHITE. NOW WE CAN PUT OUR GUNS DOWN.

NO, SARGE! THAT PARA OFFICER — WATCH OUT!

White desperately tossed his Schmeisser to Dawson —

THIS TIME I EXECUTE YOU MYSELF!

MISSED, YOU RAT! AND THIS TIME —

AIEEEE!

IT'S YOUR D-DAY TODAY — NOT MINE!

YOU GOT HIM, SARGE. HE WON'T COME BACK FROM THE DEAD LIKE YOU DID!

BACK FROM THE DEAD — BUT I'M STILL LIVING ON BORROWED TIME, WHITE!

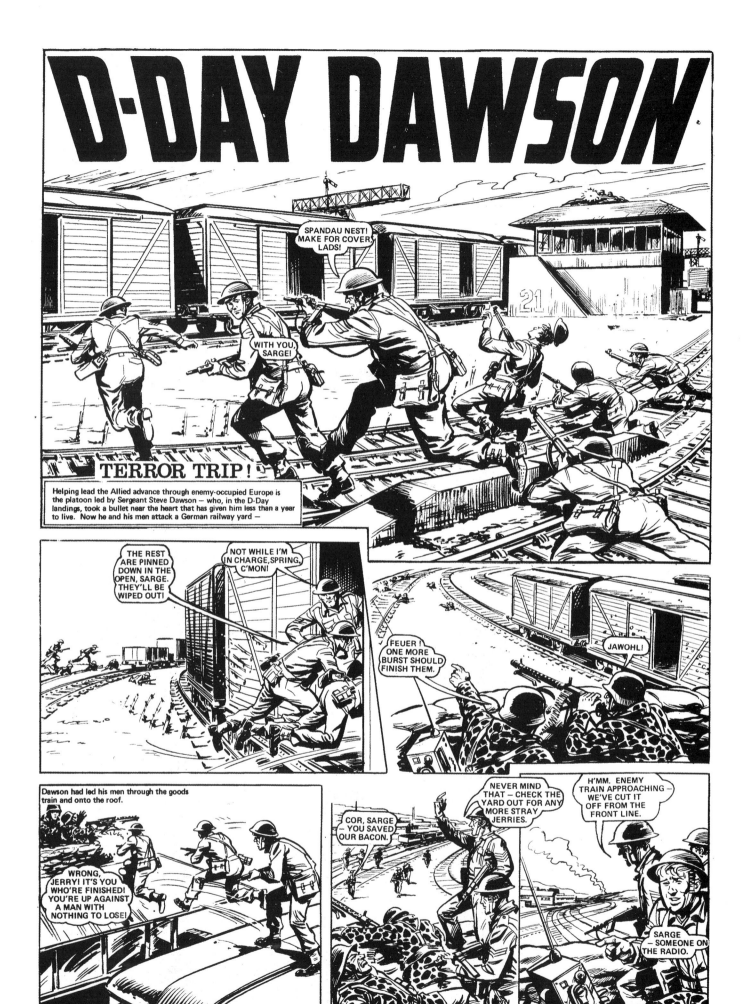

DAY OF THE EAGLE

NO TIME TO LEAVE BY THE FRONT DOOR NOW —

"MY MISSION REMAINS ON UNTIL MY TARGET IS KILLED — OR I AM!"

He is Mike Nelson — Codename: The Eagle — the Gestapo's worst nightmare and the S.O.E.'s (Special Operations Executive) top agent. He's a master of disguise, unarmed combat, espionage and assassination. Now armed with a specially adapted S.S. paratrooper sniper rifle, the Eagle's on a mission that might just end the war: TO KILL ADOLF HITLER!

'Day of the Eagle' first appeared on 8 March 1973 and quickly proved to be one of *Battle*'s most popular strips. Nelson's first adventure, presented in part here, spawned several sequels and a prequel written by writers such as John Wagner, Gerry Finley-Day, Pat Mills, Alan Hebden and Eric Hebden and artists like Pat Wright, Barrie Mitchell, Mike Dorey and Jim Watson. ✿

NOTES FROM THE FRONT LINE:

'We went for writers who had some experience of the war. The difficulty was finding someone who had interesting war memoirs, knew how to adapt them, and who could get on with these long-haired hippy types like John, Gerry and myself.

'"Day of the Eagle" was written by Major Eric Hebden, who would come in and delight us with his tales of the war; in particular he was an expert on covert warfare, and we thought he'd be perfect. He knew all the S.O.E. procedures, so we'd draw that out of him and rewrite it to give it that James Bond feeling. If you look at "Day Of The Eagle", it has all this technical stuff on the weapons... that's Eric. Then you'll see a scene where the Eagle is driving a motorbike into a lift and jumping it off a building — no prizes for guessing who wrote that bit!' — Pat Mills

WRITTEN by Eric Hebden • DRAWN by Pat Wright

DAY OF THE EAGLE

LANCASTER BOMBERS FLY ACROSS ENEMY OCCUPIED FRANCE AND WITH THEM IS A SINGLE DAKOTA. ON BOARD, SECRET AGENT MIKE NELSON — CODE NAME 'EAGLE' — WHO HAS THE MOST IMPORTANT JOB OF THE WAR — TO KILL ADOLF HITLER!

GOOD LUCK, MATE — THERE'S THE DROPPING ZONE BELOW. READY...GO!

Minutes later, after Mike had landed —

HOLD IT RIGHT THERE! DECLARE YOURSELVES —

THE DAY IS COMING...

...THE DAY OF THE EAGLE!

YOU'RE MY RESISTANCE CONTACTS ALL RIGHT. LET'S GET MOVING.

Soon, at a German road block —

HALT, PEASANT! WE HAVE ORDERS TO SEARCH EVERYONE.

ACH! SOMEONE IS HIDING IN HERE! AUS! AUS!

The second Frenchman emerged.

PARDIEU! CANNOT A MAN HAVE A SLEEP IN THE BACK OF HIS CART NOW? I WILL SPEAK TO THE MILITARY GOVERNOR ABOUT THIS!

RAISE THE BARRIER, HANS! LET THE FOOL THROUGH BEFORE HIS CHATTER RAISES THE DEAD.

The haycart carried on until it reached a nearby town.

YOUR TRICK AT THE ROADBLOCK WORKED. THEY DIDN'T CHECK ANY FURTHER!

Meanwhile, on the train, a burly S.S. paratrooper pushed past Mike —

KEEP YOUR RIFLE OUT OF MY WAY!

MY APOLOGIES!

WAIT A MINUTE! THIS RIFLE IS AN FG 42. ONLY ISSUED TO S.S. PARATROOPERS. BUT YOU ARE AN ORDINARY SOLDIER!

Mike had been specially issued with the deadly FG 42 for his mission.

YOU MUST HAVE STOLEN IT! YOU ARE UNDER ARREST!

TAKE THAT!

ACHTUNG!

Mike flung open the carriage door —

THAT RIVER DOWN BELOW — I CAN JUST DO IT!

STOP!

TIME I WAS LEAVING!

EUGH!

A sharp blow to the solar plexus —

OH, NO, YOU DON'T!

OUF!

29

34

But the Eagle was a tough quarry to take!

BACK, KRAUTS! I'M PLAYING THIS GAME FOR KEEPS!

WE HAVE THE EAGLE TRAPPED, HERR GENERALMAJOR.

JA. BUT HE IS CLEVER AND DANGEROUS. WE MUST MAKE SURE OF HIM. BRING UP A PANZER!

And soon —

FEUER!

FOUR PANZER SHELLS. NO-ONE COULD SURVIVE THAT. THE FUHRER'S ASSASSIN IS DEAD!

But after the first shell had burst, Mike had found a metal trap door —

MUNICH'S SEWER SYSTEM RUNS EVERYWHERE. IT PAYS TO DO YOUR HOMEWORK.

After a quarter of a mile, Mike surfaced in a peaceful street —

THE HOUSE OF MY CONTACT IN MUNICH. GOOD. NOW THE NAZIS THINK I'M DEAD, OPERATION EAGLE CAN PROCEED — WITHOUT INTERFERENCE!

That afternoon thousands of Germans had gathered in a giant stadium in Munich, where a massed rally was being addressed by the Fuhrer of the Third Reich — Adolf Hitler.

PEOPLE OF THE FATHERLAND! I, YOUR FUHRER, WILL LEAD YOU TO VICTORY! SOON THE NAZI JACKBOOT WILL MARCH IN TRIUMPH INTO LONDON — THEN ALL THE WORLD WILL KNOW WHO IS THE MASTER RACE!

On the rostrum were the two Gestapo men —

WE MAY BREATHE EASILY, WAGNER, NOW THAT THE EAGLE LIES WITH BROKEN WINGS BENEATH THE RUBBLE. OUR BELOVED FUHRER IS SAFE!

But few people noticed the repairman who arrived outside the rally ground —

WHAT? IS THE AIR-RAID SIREN OUT OF ORDER AGAIN?

JA, IT IS OVER-WORKED — AND LIKE ME — UNDERPAID! BUT I WILL FIX IT.

THIS AIR-RAID SIREN TOWER GIVES A GOOD VIEW OF THE PLATFORM. THE ROAR OF THE CROWD WILL COVER THE RIFLE NOISE.

The target comes into focus.

THIS IS THE MOMENT ALL MY TRAINING HAS LED UP TO. NOW, YOU MURDERING SWINE, YOU WILL PAY FOR ALL THE EVIL YOU HAVE DONE!

A tensing on the trigger.

A dart of flame leaps out.

And a bullet finds its mark!

EUGH!

THE FUHRER! MEIN GOTT! THE FUHRER IS DEAD!

RAT PACK

"YOU MEN ARE RATS — NASTY, CROOKED RATS!"

Individually, they were no better than rats, but together they put the 'rat' into 'RATATAT'! Turk, Weasel, Scarface and Dancer are four maximum-security convicts recruited by Major Taggart for a special commando unit, specialising in suicide missions deep behind enemy lines. 'Rat Pack's' thrilling adventures made it one of *Battle*'s most popular and best-remembered strips. Originally presented in stand-alone stories, 'Rat Pack' became a serial-based strip from the 100th issue of *Battle*. Stand-out artists included Carlos Ezquerra, Massimo Belardinelli, Colin Page, Mike White, Cam Kennedy, Eric Bradbury and John Cooper, while writers such as Pat Mills, John Wagner, Gerry Finley-Day, Eric Hebden and Alan Hebden shared out the scripts.

NOTES FROM THE FRONT LINE:

'We were looking for inspiration from movies like *Dirty Harry* and the spaghetti westerns; in the case of "Rat Pack", we got it with *The Dirty Dozen*. It's an archetype that's never going to go away.

'John Wagner and I came up with the basic concept and we said to Gerry Finley-Day — who was *Battle*'s unofficial third editor — "We want a Dirty Dozen", and off he went. He was such a great writer.

'It's true to say we were looking for cool artists — that was for sure. And I think with Carlos Ezquerra on "Rat Pack", you have the first really cool artist and the first really cool strip. If anybody else had drawn that, noticeably on the first episode, it wouldn't have been as successful. Carlos got it spot on, 150%. It had that spaghetti-western quality, which suited it perfectly!' – Pat Mills

WRITTEN BY Gerry Finley-Day
DRAWN BY Carlos Ezquerra

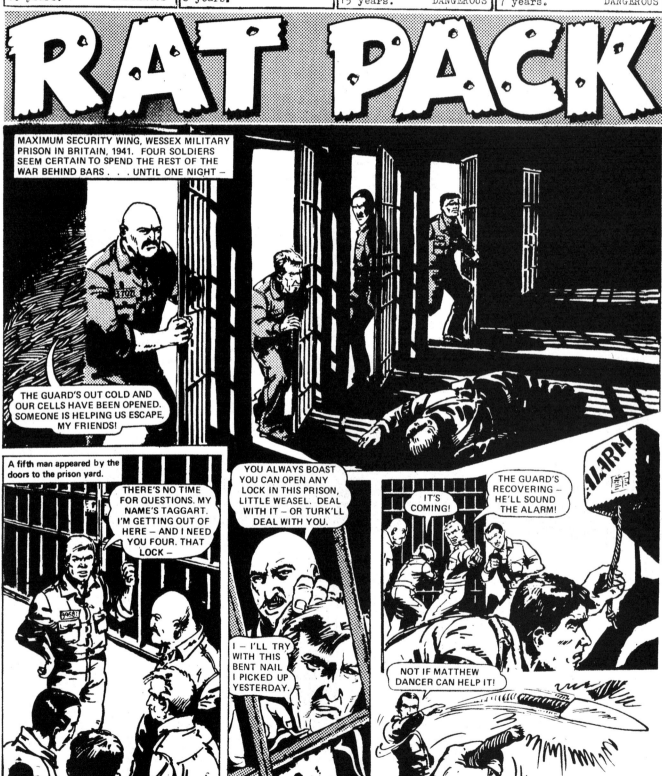

The guard was tied up. Seconds later the prisoners were outside.

NOW WHAT? THAT'S A FIFTEEN FOOT WALL TO GET OVER!

I HEAR YOU'RE QUITE AN ATHLETE, ROGAN. YOU CAN GET US OVER THERE — YOU AND OUR BIG FRIEND TURK!

The man named Taggart quickly outlined his plan.

IT'S UP TO YOU TO GRAB THE TOP OF THE WALL, ROGAN.

WITH BIG TURK AS MY LAUNCHING PAD, EH? HERE GOES —

HA — YOU LEAP LIKE A MOUNTAIN GOAT, MY FRIEND!

Using Rogan as a human ladder, the other prisoners began to scramble up.

GOOD WORK — I WAS COUNT-ING ON YOU, ROGAN.

YOU'VE THOUGHT OF EVERYTHING, TAGGART!

THERE'S OUR GETAWAY VEHICLE. FOLLOW ME — FAST!

BLIMEY! THE PRISON SIREN'S SOUNDING! WE WERE ONLY JUST IN TIME!

A frantic hour's drive along country roads and then Taggart turned off towards a deserted farm.

I DON'T UNDERSTAND THIS MAN TAGGART. HE ORGANISES A WELL-PLANNED ESCAPE FOR US — BUT WE HAVE NEVER MET HIM BEFORE...

YET HE SEEMS TO KNOW ALL ABOUT US.

STOP YOUR BELLY-ACHING! POOF! WHY SHOULD WE CARE WHY HE HELPS US? THE IMPORTANT THING IS WE ARE FREE!

40

The prisoners thought long and hard. At last —

H'MM. WE LIKE THE SOUND OF THIS, TAGGART. ROGAN AND I WILL JOIN YOUR LITTLE "RAT PACK".

I DO NOT LIKE YOU, TAGGART, AND ONE DAY, MAYBE I KILL YOU. BUT FOR NOW I AGREE — AND SO DOES THE LITTLE WEASEL HERE.

WOT — ME? OH — Y — YES, TURK.

OPERATION BIG KARL.

GOOD! THEN HERE'S OUR FIRST TARGET. BIG KARL — A SIXTEEN INCH, LONG RANGE GERMAN GUN SITED ON THE FRENCH COAST. THE KILLER OF TWENTY OF OUR SHIPS. THE RAF HAVE TRIED TO BOMB IT AND FAILED. NOW IT'S UP TO US.

THIS JOB COULD BE SUICIDE. BUT IF ANY OF YOU HAVE IDEAS ABOUT USING IT TO ESCAPE — FORGET 'EM! YOU MAY BE TOUGH, BUT YOU'LL FIND I'M A LOT TOUGHER!

Two weeks later, a British Dakota approached the French coast —

NEARING THE DROPPING ZONE, MEN. STAND BY!

ACTION AGAIN! I'M LOOKING FORWARD TO THIS.

TURK, TOO. SOON WE PUT THESE WEAPONS TO GOOD USE!

I'M SORRY, MAJOR TAGGART. WIND'S TOO HIGH FOR YOUR MEN TO JUMP. YOU'LL HAVE TO CANCEL THE MISSION.

MY MEN ARE PREPARED FOR ANYTHING. WE'RE NOT TURNING BACK NOW!

41

MAJOR TAGGART. Special Services Commando. Leader and founder of RAT.PACK. No mission too dangerous for this man.

RAT PACK

THE CONVICT COMMANDOS ON A SUICIDE MISSION—TO DESTROY A HUGE GERMAN GUN... OR DIE!

37021

KABUL HASAN. Cyprus Rifles. Known as "the Turk". Court martialled for attacking officers in fit of rage. 10 years.   DANGEROUS

37194

RONALD WEASEL. Kent Infantry. Expert Safebreaker. Court martialled robbery Army Paymaster's Office. 8 years.

36616

IAN "SCARFACE" ROGAN. Highland Infantry. Brilliant athlete. Court martialled for desertion. 15 years.   DANGEROUS

34024

MATTHEW DANCER. Commandos. Deadly with a knife. Born marksman. Court martialled for looting. 7 years.   DANGEROUS

44

45

LISTEN, TAGGART. STRANGE NOISES COME FROM BEHIND US.

KILLER HOUNDS!

THAT'S ONE OF THE BRUTES! BUT THE TURK'S HAD IT.

AHH!

PAH! A HOUND IS NO MATCH FOR TURK!

LET'S GET MOVING.

WE CAN'T. LOOK — LIGHTS! THE GERMANS ARE ALL AROUND US NOW.

WE SHOULD'VE SURRENDERED THE FIRST TIME.

WE'RE NOT FINISHED YET, WEASEL. DANCER — YOU GOT YOUR KNIFE HANDY?

ALWAYS.

Taggart led Rat Pack into the river.

CUT THE TUBES OF THE GAS MASKS — WE'LL USE 'EM AS BREATHING TUBES. TURK — PUT THE BODY OF THAT DOG ON THE BRIDGE.

Seconds later . . .

SO, THEY HAVE KILLED MY DOGS! THE SWINE!

THEY ARE STILL AROUND — I FEEL IT! BUT WHERE?

The sentries did not hear Rat Pack's stealthy approach

UUURGH!

SWEET DREAMS, MY FRIENDS!

WHAT A MONSTER! NO WONDER IT COULDN'T BE BOMBED FROM THE AIR WITH THE CLIFF OVER HANG PROTECTING IT.

THIS ROPE'LL COME IN HANDY.

I'LL GO DOWN FIRST WITH THE STICK BOMBS, YOU MEN FOLLOW ON MY HEELS.

PRESENT FOR YOU, FRIENDS!

HIMMEL!

AIEEE!

When the rest swung down

MORE JERRIES COMING! GUARD THE TUNNEL. ROGAN AND I WILL TAKE CARE OF BIG KARL.

THE REST OF THE STICK GRENADES HAVE TO BE DROPPED INSIDE THE GUN.

ROGAN MOVES LIKE A CAT! I PICKED MY CLIMBER WELL.

LOOK OUT!

Dancer's knife whirled through the air

UGGH!

JUST IN TIME!

RAT PACK

MAJOR TAGGART. Special Services Commando. Leader and founder of RAT PACK. No mission too dangerous for this man.

KABUL HASAN. Cyprus Rifles. Known as "the Turk". Court martialled for attacking officers in fit of rage. 10 years. DANGEROUS

RONALD WEASEL. Kent Inf. Expert Safebreaker. Court martialled robbery Army Paymaster's Office. 8 years.

IAN "SCARFACE" ROGAN. Highland Infantry. Brilliant athlete. Court martialled for desertion. 15 years. DANGEROUS

MATTHEW DANCER. Commandos. Deadly with a knife. Born marksman. Court martialled for looting. 7 years. DANGEROUS

IF THERE'S A WAY IN, GENERAL — WE'LL FIND IT!

THAT'S THE RENATA OIL REFINERY MAJOR TAGGART — FIVE MILES OFF VENICE. GUARDED BY THE TOUGHEST S.S. TROOPS IN EUROPE, IT PROCESSES TEN POINT THREE PERCENT OF THE OIL THAT KEEPS THE GERMAN WAR MACHINE MOVING. RAT PACK ARE GOING TO SMASH IT INTO THE GROUND!

MAIN GATES

ADMIN BLOCK

GUARD HOUSE

SECURITY BARRIER

CAR PARK

BOILER HOUSE

TOP SECRET INSTALLATION PURPOSE UNKNOWN

FIRE STATION

LORRY PARK

GARAGE AND WORKSHOP

STORAGE TANK

STORAGE TANK

STORAGE TANK

STO TAN

STORA

CRACKING PLANT

Later, at night —

PASS IN ORDER! ENTER!

But Rat Pack had found their way in. It was thick, black, and choking — but it was the only way!

THAT WAS THE CHECK-POINT ON THE MAIN GATE. WE'RE MOVING ON AGAIN.

50

Soon –

WE'RE SLOWING DOWN – THIS TIME FOR KEEPS. RIGHT, TURK – THE HATCH!

ALL CLEAR.

RIGHT, OUT OF THE SUB-AQUA GEAR – AND QUICK ABOUT IT.

A MESSY START TO A MISSION, TAGGART.

Suddenly –

GERMAN COLUMN – FREEZE.

BLIMEY! MY FOOT'S SLIPPED!

WHAT – HIMMEL! SABOTEURS!

YOU FOOL, WEASEL! WASTE 'EM!

The fight was short –

But deadly!

LOOKS LIKE A PLANT FOR PROCESSING EXPERIMENTAL ROCKET FUELS.

VITAL TO THE NAZIS. OKAY, TIME'S RUNNING OUT, MEN, SO . . .

. . . LET'S START THE ACTION!

WITH PLEASURE!

AAAGH!

The soldiers outside ran forward, but —

WER DA . . . AIEE!

WE SAID WE DIDN'T WANT TO BE DISTURBED, KRAUT!

MORE OF 'EM ON THE PLATFORM. GET ROUND BEHIND, ROGAN.

Rogan summoned all his strength for a mighty leap.

AAH!

SURPRISE! SURPRISE!

BEHIND US — ARGH!

LISTEN . . . THE DOORS! THE KRAUTS MUST HAVE A BATTERING RAM. THEY'LL BREAK IN!

WEASEL! UP HERE AND TAKE A LOOK AT THESE CONTROLS!

THIS IS THE CONTROL PANEL FOR THE ROCKET FUEL. NOW IF I JUST ADJUST THE INFLOW AND SHUT OFF THE OUTLET . . .

IT'LL BURST THE TANK? RIGHT — DO IT!

THEY'RE NEARLY THROUGH — HURRY!

I — I'M DOING ME BEST! THE FUEL LEVEL'S RISING!

BATTLE MASTER PLAN

NAVIGATION LIGHT

DORSAL STABILISER FIN

ANTENNA

TAIL LIGHT

AFT FUEL TANK

RADIO BAY

ANTI-GLARE BLINDS

TAILWHEEL RETRACTING MECHANISM

EXHAUST WASTE OUTLET

FOUR "STAGGERED" BROWNINGS IN EACH WING

WHEEL WELL

AMMUNITION FEED CHUTES

NAVIGATION LIGHT

UNDERWING SHACKLES FOR EITHER 500- OR 1,000-LB. BOMB

EARLY-TYPE 4.5-IN. 3-TUBE ROCKET LAUNCHER FOR GROUND ATTACK OPERATIONS

TELESCOPIC UNDERCARRIAGE (9 INS. SHORTER WHEN RETRACTED)

THE Republic Thunderbolt was the largest and heaviest single-seat fighter ever built, but this was no disadvantage. It played an impressive part in World War II in almost every theatre of war.

The Thunderbolt made its operational début with the U.S. Air Force in Britain in 1943, and proved itself as an efficient high-altitude escort plane. Luftwaffe pilots soon learnt to fear these stocky aircraft, which could absorb an immense amount of damage and still return to base.

On the way back from escorting the high-flying Liberators and Flying Fortresses, the Thunderbolts would fly very low and use their ammunition up on ground targets. In this way, almost by accident, the Thunderbolt discovered its most famous rôle : that of fighter-bomber.

With its load of bombs and rockets,

REPUBLIC P.47D "THUNDERBOLT"

LARGEST SINGLE-SEAT FIGHTER EVER BUILT

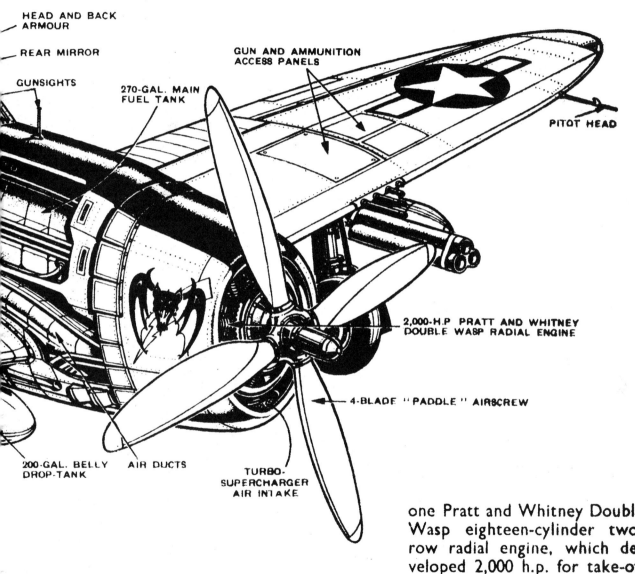

HEAD AND BACK ARMOUR

REAR MIRROR

GUNSIGHTS

270-GAL. MAIN FUEL TANK

GUN AND AMMUNITION ACCESS PANELS

PITOT HEAD

2,000-H.P PRATT AND WHITNEY DOUBLE WASP RADIAL ENGINE

4-BLADE "PADDLE" AIRSCREW

200-GAL. BELLY DROP-TANK

AIR DUCTS

TURBO-SUPERCHARGER AIR INTAKE

the Thunderbolt played a big part in softening up Hitler's European defences in preparation for D-Day. Between D-Day and the end of the War in Europe, Thunderbolts destroyed 86,000 railway coaches, 9,000 engines, 68,000 motor-cars and lorries, and 6,000 armoured vehicles in Germany alone !

The Thunderbolt was powered by one Pratt and Whitney Double Wasp eighteen-cylinder two-row radial engine, which developed 2,000 h.p. for take-off and 23,000 h.p. at 31,000 feet with turbo-supercharging.

Its maximum speed was 429 m.p.h. at 30,000 feet, and 350 m.p.h. at sea level. It had a service ceiling of 40,000 feet and a range of 950 miles.

The Thunderbolt carried an armament of six or eight Browning machine-guns, and 2,500 lb. of bombs or ten HVAR missiles.

JOHNNY RED

"HAVE SOME LEAD FROM JOHNNY RED!"

On a cargo ship bound for Murmansk, hot-headed but brilliant flyer Johnny Redburn, dishonourably discharged from the R.A.F., thought his flying career was as good as dead until the day he hijacked a ship-launched Hurricane and single-handedly took on a squadron of Stukas and Junkers.

Now he's a signed-up member of the Soviet Union's 5th Air Brigade, 'Falcon Squadron', and fighting a war on the bitter Russian front.

Lasting ten years and over 500 episodes, 'Johnny Red' was arguably *Battle*'s most popular strip. Created by writer Tom Tully and artist Joe Colquhoun (who drew the first 100 episodes) it ran from January 1977's issue #100 of *Battle* until January 1987,

during which time Carlos Pino replaced the strip's longest-serving artist, John Cooper. ✪

NOTES FROM THE FRONT LINE:
'"Johnny Red" was written by Tom Tully, who, despite being very marinated in old-style comic traditions, still managed to adapt successfully to *Battle*'s new approach. He would take the time to research Leningrad, Stalingrad and so forth: prior to *Battle*, research was pretty much non-existent in British comics. I think that shows in some of the comics before *Battle*. "Johnny Red" is actually very authentic — there *were* British pilots flying on the Russian front. It's one of the ironies of war comics that real life is often very similar in style.' — Pat Mills

WRITTEN BY Tom Tully
DRAWN BY Joe Colquhoun

COME ON, CLIMB! IF IT NEEDS RAW MUSCLE TO FLY YOU, I'VE GOT ALL YOU CAN TAKE!

61

Johnny could have pancaked the Hurricane in the sea, and waited to be picked up by one of the convoy ships...

BUT THEN PEOPLE WOULD START ASKING AWKWARD QUESTIONS — LIKE WHO GAVE ME PERMISSION TO BORROW AN EXPENSIVE HURRICANE...!

NOT A KITE IN THE SKY! THE JERRIES HAVE CALLED IT A DAY! STONE ME, WHAT THE HELL DO I DO NOW?

But as the coastline of the Kola peninsula slid under the Hurricane's wings...

HEADING INTO A BANK OF FOG... A RIGHT OLD RUSSIAN PEA-SOUPER! THEY WARNED US WE COULD EXPECT WEATHER CONDITIONS LIKE THIS!

...SO I'LL HEAD FOR THE RUSSIAN MAINLAND! IF I CAN SAVE THE HURRI TO FIGHT AGAIN, IT MIGHT CONVINCE THE R.A.F. THAT THEY MADE A BIG MISTAKE WHEN THEY COURT-MARTIALLED JOHNNY RED!

NO NEED TO PANIC, THOUGH! IF I HEAD DUE SOUTH, I'M BOUND TO HIT ONE OF THE BIG RUSSIAN AIRFIELDS AROUND MURMANSK...!

But, an hour later, as the fog began to clear...

Then...through a break in the snow-storm...

WHATEVER IT IS, IT'LL HAVE TO DO!

...NOW I'VE GOT SNOW TO CONTEND WITH! CAN'T SEE A THING, EXCEPT MARSHES AND PINE FORESTS!

I CAN SEE A CLEARING, DOWN THERE — HUTS OF SOME KIND! MAYBE IT'S THE OUT-SKIRTS OF A RUSSKI VILLAGE...!

...Johnny couldn't have seen the outlines of aircraft, parked under the pine trees...!

...or the figures that huddled within a patched-up tent!

THEN HE HAS CHOSEN TO DIE! HAAAIEEEE!

...HE'S COMING IN TO LAND! BUT IT IS NOT ONE OF OURS! THE DESIGN IS TOO ADVANCED!

A GERMAN, PERHAPS?

DA, THAT IS IT! PROBABLY DAMAGED! HE HAS CHOSEN OUR BASE TO MAKE AN EMERGENCY LANDING!

STOP, YAKOB! THE CRAZY FOOL WILL KILL THAT PILOT BEFORE HE CAN BE QUESTIONED!

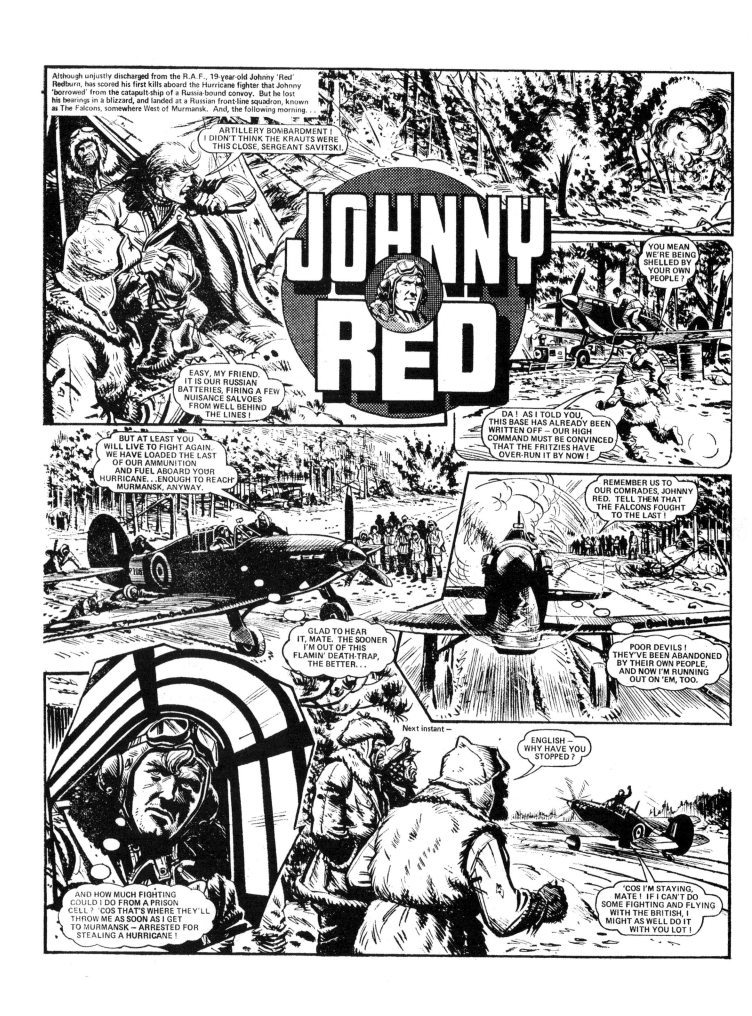

BUT WHAT ARE WE TO FIGHT WITH? EVEN OUR FOOD IS ALMOST GONE!

AND EVEN IF WE COULD CONTACT THE SUPPLY DEPOT, THEY WOULD NOT WASTE VALUABLE WAR MATERIAL ON MEN WHO ARE CONSIDERED DEAD!

THEN IF YOUR FLAMIN' BRASS-HATS WON'T SEND US ANY SUPPLIES, WE'LL RUDDY WELL FETCH 'EM OURSELVES!

Moments later, as Johnny outlined his plan in the Falcons' operations hut...

...YOU SAY THAT THIS HIGHWAY — ABOUT SIXTY KILOMETRES FROM HERE — IS ONE OF THE MAIN SUPPLY-ROUTES TO THE MOSCOW AND LENINGRAD FRONTS FROM THE PORT OF MURMANSK?

DA! THE CONVOYS ROLL BY NIGHT AND DAY, CARRYING MILLIONS OF TONS OF SUPPLIES TO OUR BESIEGED CITIES!

OKAY! THERE SHOULD BE JUST ENOUGH FUEL IN THE FLIGHT-TRUCK TO MAKE IT TO THE HIGHWAY AND INTERCEPT ONE OF THE CONVOYS JUST HERE...WHERE IT PASSES THROUGH THE EDGE OF THE FOREST!

MURMANSK

KOLA

Yakotsk

After Johnny had outlined the rest of his plan...

IT IS NOT A PLAN... IT IS SUICIDE! IF WE ARE CAUGHT STEALING SUPPLIES FROM ONE OF OUR OWN CONVOYS, IT WILL MEAN THE FIRING-SQUAD, FOR ALL OF US!

DA, KRASOV! THIS JOHNNY RED IS CRAZY...

...BUT IT IS THE KIND OF MADNESS THAT MAY GIVE US ANOTHER CHANCE. WE ARE TRAINED TO FIGHT IN THE AIR, COMRADES...NOT DIE LIKE PIGS ON THE GROUND!

YAKOB IS RIGHT! WHAT HAVE WE TO LOSE?

I AM WITH YOU, COMRADE..!

And soon...

ZA RODINU — FOR RUSSIA!

LOOKS LIKE THE FALCONS ARE FIGHTING BACK, JOHNNY RED! LET'S JUST HOPE YOU CAN FINISH WHAT YOU'VE STARTED.

Nearly two hours later...

WE ARE JUST IN TIME, COMRADES! SEE — ANOTHER CONVOY HEADING SOUTH FROM MURMANSK!

THREE OF THOSE TRUCKS WILL CONTAIN ENOUGH SUPPLIES TO KEEP US FLYING FOR A FEW MORE DAYS...

As the Falcons parked the truck in the forest, just off the main highway...

THERE GOES JOHNNY RED!

HURRY, COMRADES! WE MUST BE IN POSITION BEFORE HE MAKES HIS ATTACK...